THE TWO-iN-ONE CAPTAiN UNDERPANTS EXTRA-CRUNCHY BOOK O' FUN 2

BY DAV PILKEY

The Blue Sky Press • An Imprint of Scholastic Inc. • New York

For Elizabeth and Rachel

THE BLUE SKY PRESS

This book was originally published as
The All New Captain Underpants Extra-Crunchy Book O' Fun 2
by the Blue Sky Press in 2002.

ISBN-13: 978-0-439-89209-4
ISBN-10: 0-439-89209-0

12 11 10 9 8 7 6 5 4 3 2 1   7 8 9 10 11 12/0

Printed in the United States of America   40

This edition first printing, October 2007

WEDGIE-POWERED WORD FIND

Try to find the names below in the puzzle on the right.
Look up, down, backwards, and diagonally.

CHARACTER NAME BONUS QUIZ:

How well do you know your UNDERPANTS?
Draw lines from the <u>first</u> names in Chart A
to the matching <u>last</u> names in Chart B.

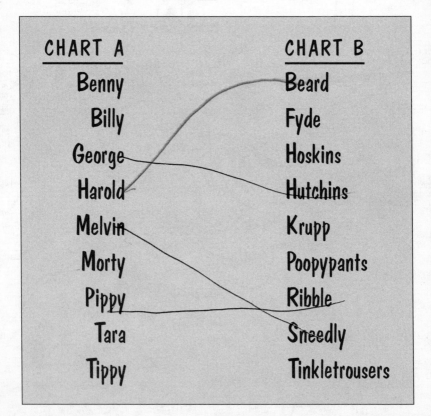

CHART A	CHART B
Benny	Beard
Billy	Fyde
George	Hoskins
Harold	Hutchins
Melvin	Krupp
Morty	Poopypants
Pippy	Ribble
Tara	Sneedly
Tippy	Tinkletrousers

```
S T N A P Y P O O P
R U O R L Y H Q N A
E G N L V X T V F F
S N I H C T U H L Z
U B V M A L O E S A
O A L F O S G D R J
R U E C K R R A Q E
T F M I O A T D D I
E S N E E D L Y V E
L S G B L O F L R S
K Q F F R B P C P U
N S E A E R B I C R
I A H N Y P P I T Z
T X N M J P P U R K
K Y Q B Y R Z X D C
```

(Answer on
page 93)

HOW TO DRAW
CAPTAIN UNDERPANTS

1.

2.

3.

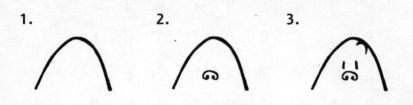

4.

5.

6.

7.

8.

9.

10.

6

11.

12.

13.

14.

15.

16.

7

PERPLEXING PEEWEE-POWERED PUZZLE

ACROSS

3. Captain Underpants fights for Truth, Justice, and all that is Pre-Shrunk and _____!
5. A flushable porcelain bowl.
7. "Tra-_____-Laaaaa!"
8. Super Diaper Baby's archenemy is _____ Doo-Doo.
9. Captain Underpants is nicknamed the _____ Warrior.
10. Super Diaper Baby's best friend is Diaper _____.
11. The only five-letter word (starting with an "s") to appear twice in the last six clues.
14. Watch out for the Wicked Wedgie _____!
15. Liquid spray _____ is the enemy of underwear.

DOWN

1. The three evil space guys were named _____, Klax, and Jennifer.
2. New Swissland's most famous scientist is Professor _____.

3. Three cheers for _____ Underpants!

4. The Bride of _____ Potty.

6. Beware of the _____-Toilet 2000!

10. Billy Hoskins is better known as Super _____ Baby.

12. Don't spill the Extra-Strength Super _____ Juice!

13. Ms. _____ turned into the Wicked Wedgie Woman.

(Answer on page 93)

HOW TO DRAW
MR. KRUPP

1.

2.

3.

4.

5.

6.

7.

8.

9.

10.

11.

12.

13.

14.

15.

16.

Help George and Harold Get into Their Tree House

(Answer on page 94)

LAFFS

Q) Why did the cookie cry?
A) Because his mom had been a wafer so long.

"Knock knock."
"Who's there?"
"Olive Toop."
"Olive Toop who?"
"Well so do I, but you don't hear *me* braggin' about it!"

Ms. Ribble: Harold, if I gave you two goldfish, and Melvin gave you four goldfish, how many would you have?
Harold: Eleven.
Ms. Ribble: *ELEVEN*?!!? Hah! You're *WRONG*, bub!
Harold: No, *you're* wrong. I already have five goldfish back at home!

George: Excuse me, mister, I'd like to buy some toilet paper.
Grocery store clerk: What color would you like?
George: Just give me white. I'll color it myself!

Q) What do you get when you cross a porcupine with a great white shark?
A) As far away as possible.

HOW TO DRAW GEORGE

1.

2.

3.

4.

5.

6.

7.

8.

9.

10.

11.

12.

13.

14.

15.

16.

HOW TO DRAW HAROLD

1. 2. 3. 4.

5. 6.

7. 8.

9. 10.

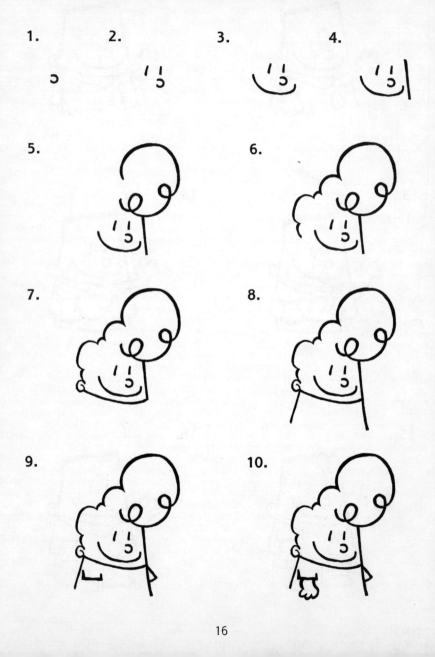

11.

12.

13.

14.

15.

16.

NOW YOU CAN BE THE STAR
OF YOUR OWN SUPER-CHEESY
CAPTAIN UNDERPANTS STORY!

Before you read the story on the following pages, go through and find all the blanks. Below each blank is a small description of what you need to write in the blank. Just fill in the blank with an appropriate word.

For example, if the blank looks like this:

_____, you would think up an adjective and
(an adjective)
put it in the blank like this: ___Snotty___ .
(an adjective)

Remember, don't read the story first. It's more fun if you go through and fill in the blanks first, THEN read the story.

When you're done, follow the instructions at the bottom of each page to complete the illustrations. Cool, huh?

JUST FOR REMINDERS:
a **Verb** is an <u>action</u> word (like jump, swim, kick, squish, run, etc.)
an **Adjective** is a word that <u>describes</u> a person, place, or thing (lumpy, dumb, purple, hairy, etc.)

THE INCREDIBLY STUPID ADVENTURE OF
CAPTAIN UNDERPANTS

This is George Beard, Harold Hutchins,

and _____ _____.
      (your first name)   (your last name)

George is the one on the left with the tie and

the flat-top. Harold is the one on the right

with the T-shirt and the bad haircut.

_____ is the one in the middle
      (your first name)

with the _____ _____
              (an adjective)   (article of clothing)

and the _____ _____.
              (an adjective)   (body part or parts)

Remember that now.

↑
(Draw yourself here)

One day, George, Harold, and _____
(your first name)
were at school when suddenly, an evil _____
(an adjective)
villain _____ through the door and
(a verb ending in "ed")
roared like a ferocious _____ .
(a harmless insect)

"My name is Commander_____
(a gross adjective)
_____!" shouted the villain. "And I've come
(a gross thing)
to destroy all the _____ in the world!"
(smelly things)

Commander_____ _____
(the gross adjective and thing you used above)
grabbed a_____ and started hitting
(a piece of furniture)
_____ on the _____ with it.
(your gym teacher's name)   (a body part)

"Oh no!" cried_____ . "That villain is
(your first name)
going to hurt the poor _____!"
(the piece of furniture you used above)

(Draw yourself here)   (Draw your evil villain here)

20

"We've got to stop that monster!" cried

George. He reached into his _____ ,

(an article of clothing)

grabbed a/an _____ _____ ,

(an adjective)   (something big)

and threw it at the villain.

Harold found a/an _____ in his

(something bigger)

_____ , so he threw that, too. Finally,

(an article of clothing)

_____ reached into his/her_____ ,

(your name)   (an article of clothing)

pulled out a/an _____ _____ ,

(an adjective)   (the biggest thing you can think of)

and threw that as well.

But nothing seemed to stop the _____

(a disgusting adjective)

Commander_____ _____!

(the gross adjective and thing you used twice on page 20)

(Draw yourself here)   (Draw the stuff you are throwing through the air)   (Draw your evil villain here)

"This looks like a job for Captain Underpants!"

shouted _____.
        (your first name)

Suddenly, Captain Underpants _____
                                (a verb ending in "ed")

into the school. "Hi," said Captain Underpants.

"How's your _____ _____
             (an adjective)   (an animal)

_____ today?"
(a part of the body)

"That doesn't make any sense," said Harold.

"Who cares?" said _____ . "We've got
                    (your first name)

to stop that villain!" So Captain Underpants

grabbed a baseball bat and hit Commander

_____ _____ over the
(the gross adjective and thing you used twice on page 20)

head repeatedly.

(Draw yourself here)   (Draw your evil villain here)

22

HERE COMES THE BAT, MAN!

(Draw your villain here. Make him about the same height
as Captain Underpants. If you need help, look at the
Flip-O-Ramas between pages 45 and 89 for inspiration.)

HERE COMES THE BAT, MAN!

(Draw your villain here. Make him about the same height
as Captain Underpants. If you need help, look at the
Flip-O-Ramas between pages 45 and 89 for inspiration.)

"Holy _____ _____!" shouted
(a verb ending in "ing")   (an animal)

George. "Captain Underpants has defeated

Commander _____ _____!"
(the gross adjective and thing you used twice on page 20)

"Let's celebrate by eating _____ servings of
(a number)

_____ _____ and drinking _____ cups
(an adjective)   (something gross)   (a number)

of _____ _____ ," said Harold.
(an adjective)   (a disgusting liquid)

"That sounds delicious," said _____ .
(your first name)

"Just be sure to sprinkle some _____
(a gross adjective)

_____ on my food, and add a slice of
(creepy things)

_____ to my _____ ."
(something gross)   (the disgusting liquid you used above)

(Draw yourself sitting here)   (Draw your defeated villain lying here)

26

(Answer on page 94)

HOW TO DRAW WEDGIE WOMAN

1. 2. 3. 4.

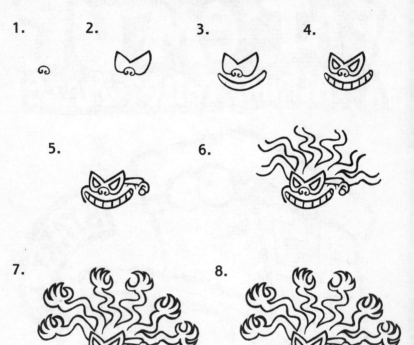

5. 6.

7. 8.

9. 10.

11.

12.

13.

14.

15.

16.

HOW TO DRAW ZORX, KLAX, AND JENNIFER

1.

2.

3.

4.

5.

6.

7.

8.

9.

10.

11.

12.

13.

14.

15.

16.

FUN WITH ACCESSORIES

1. Add eyelashes!

2. Add lipstick!

3. Add a bow!

4a.

Zorxette

4b.

5a.

Klaxette

5b.

6a.

Jenniferette

6b.

(Answer on page 95)

(Answer on page 95)

Q) Why does Ms. Ribble keep a stick of dynamite in her auto emergency kit?
A) In case she gets a flat and needs to blow up one of her tires.

Q) Why was the mushroom always invited to parties?
A) Because he was a fungi!

Q) What's the difference between Mr. Krupp and an elephant?
A) One is huge, wrinkled, has a goofy nose, and smells terrible . . . and the other is an elephant!

Q) What's green, cold, and topped with whipped cream?
A) A snot-fudge sundae.

Q) What's invisible and smells like bananas?
A) Monkey burps!

Q) What's the difference between pea soup and popcorn?
A) Anyone can pop corn!

Tommy: Mommy, can I lick the bowl?
Mommy: No, Tommy, you have to flush like everybody else!

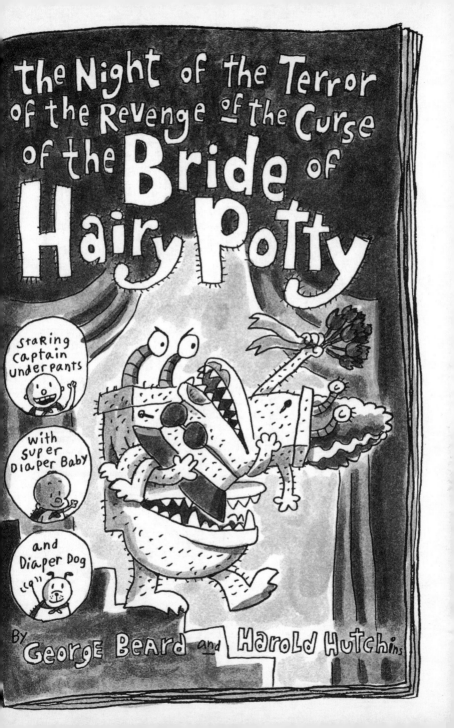

FLIP-O-RAMA #1

Pages 45 and 47.

Remember, Flip <u>only</u> page 45. While you are Fliping, be shure you can see the Pitcher on page 45 and the one on Page 47.

If you Flip Quickly, the two pitchers will start to Look Like ~~two~~ <u>One</u> Animated pitcher.

Left Hand Here

Smack Attack

RIGHT
THUMB
Here

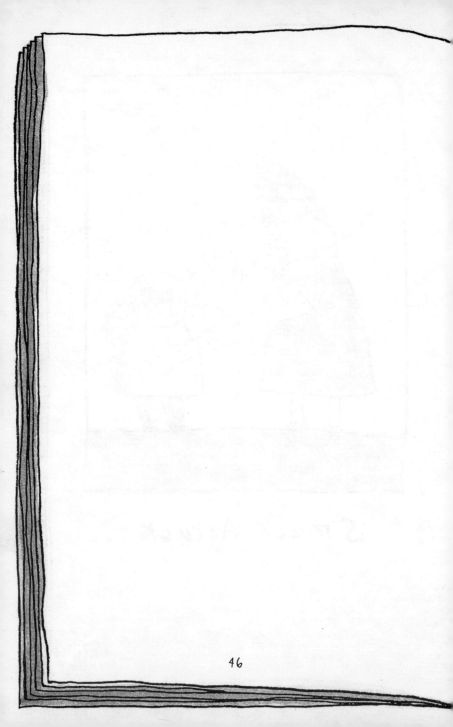

Smack Attack

I am woman,
See me punch

51

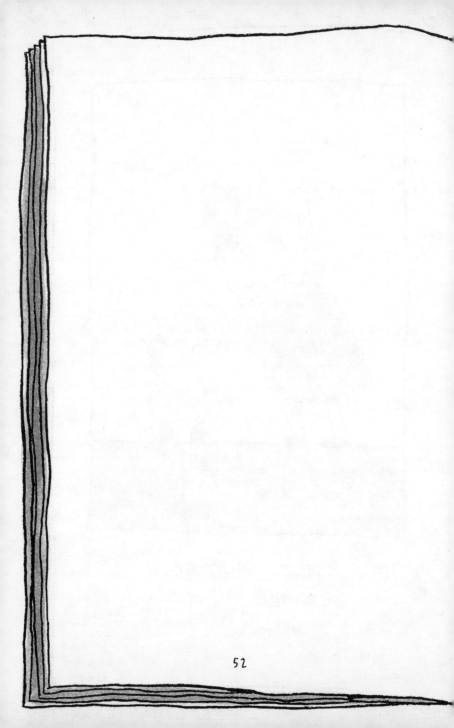

I am woman,
see me punch

Hairy Potty's Pieces began to morph together.
And DR. Frankenbeanies cloning machine began to work.
LAdy DNA
Hairy Potty DNA
ZAP
there she is!
She's Growing!

welcome to the world, baby! I am your creater, and you Shall obey me. You Shall atend to my every wim.
Uh... master?
First, go into the Kichen and wash all of the dishes. And bake me a pie while your at it. Then mop the Floors and wash the windows and sow my socks and iron my Pants and cook my dinner and make my bed and...
Hey master... um--- Hey master???

...And if you do a good job, I'll let you give me a back-Rub when your done!
m-m-m-m-master?
NOW GO, Woman! Do my Bidding!
-ULP
You see, Jeff, You have to be Firm with women or else they'll...
HEY!
FLIP-O-RAMA
Left Hand Here

strechy
strechy

61

RIGHT THUMB Here

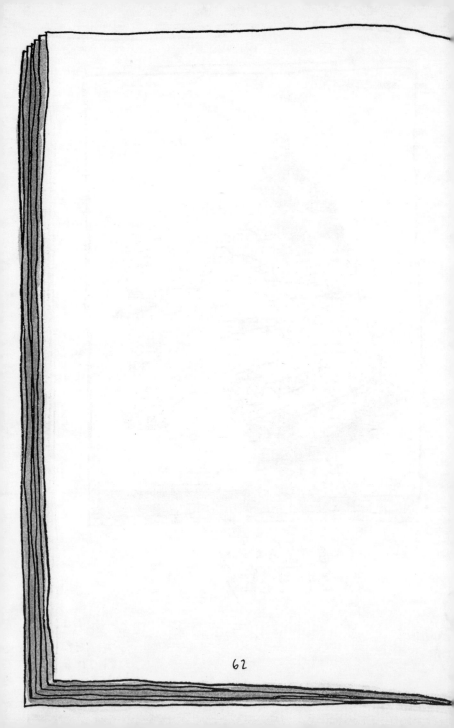

Strechy
strechy

Jumping rope
with a dope.

65

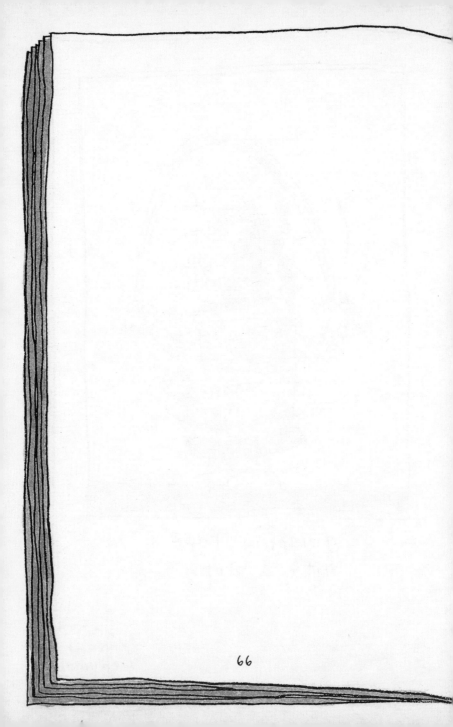

66

Jumping rope
with a dope.

Then it was off to vegas for a Romantic wedding
Do you take this toiLet to be your LawFuLLy wedded ToiLet?
O.K.
You may now FLush the Bride
FinaLy, it was time For...
MASS DESTRUCTSion
This Looks Like a JoB For....

Inflate-a-Bowl

RIGHt
THuMB
Here

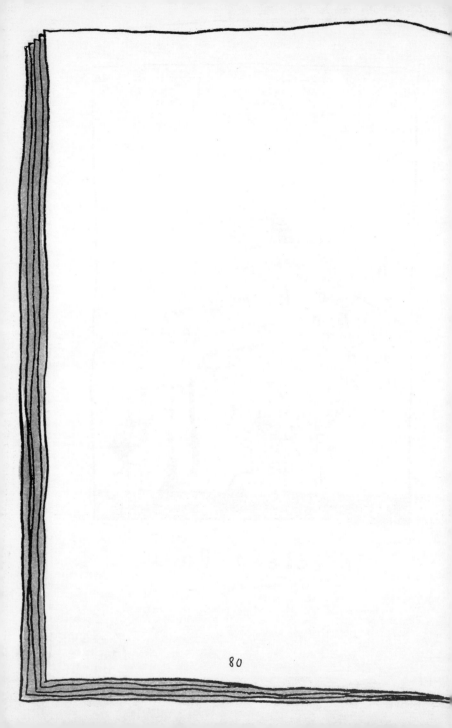

InFlate-a-Bowl

OH NO!!! Super Diaper Baby and Diaper Dog Both got eaten--- and Captain Underpants was still Too Weak to Fight. Is this the end for our heros?

Hammer time

Right thumB Here

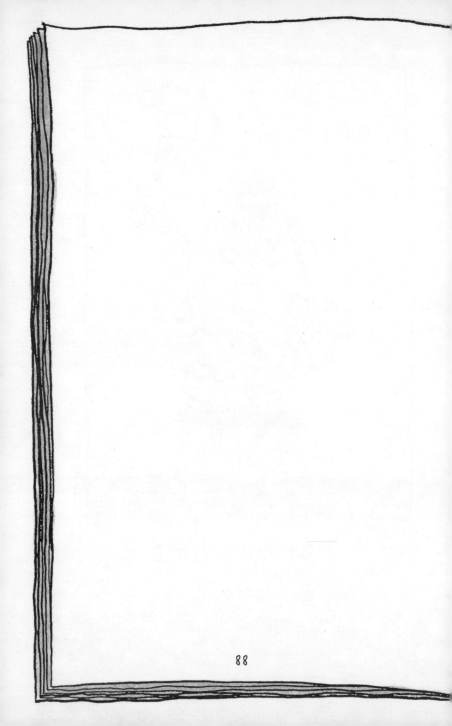

Hammer time

ANSWERS

Word Find
p. 4

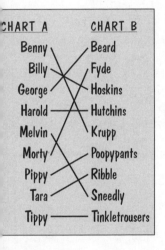

Bonus Quiz
p. 4

Crossword
p. 8

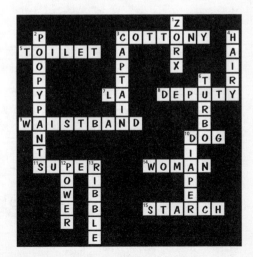

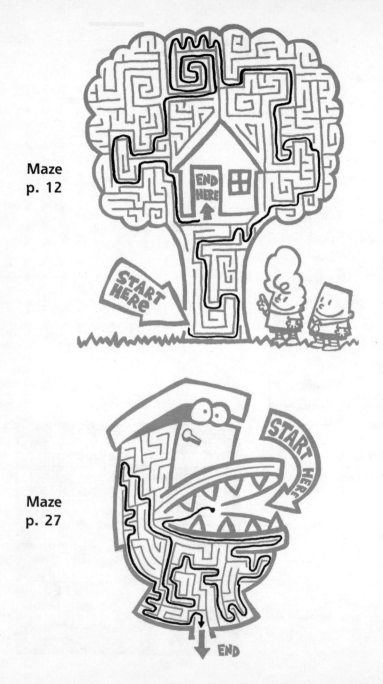

Maze
p. 12

Maze
p. 27

**Maze
p. 33**

**Maze
p. 34**

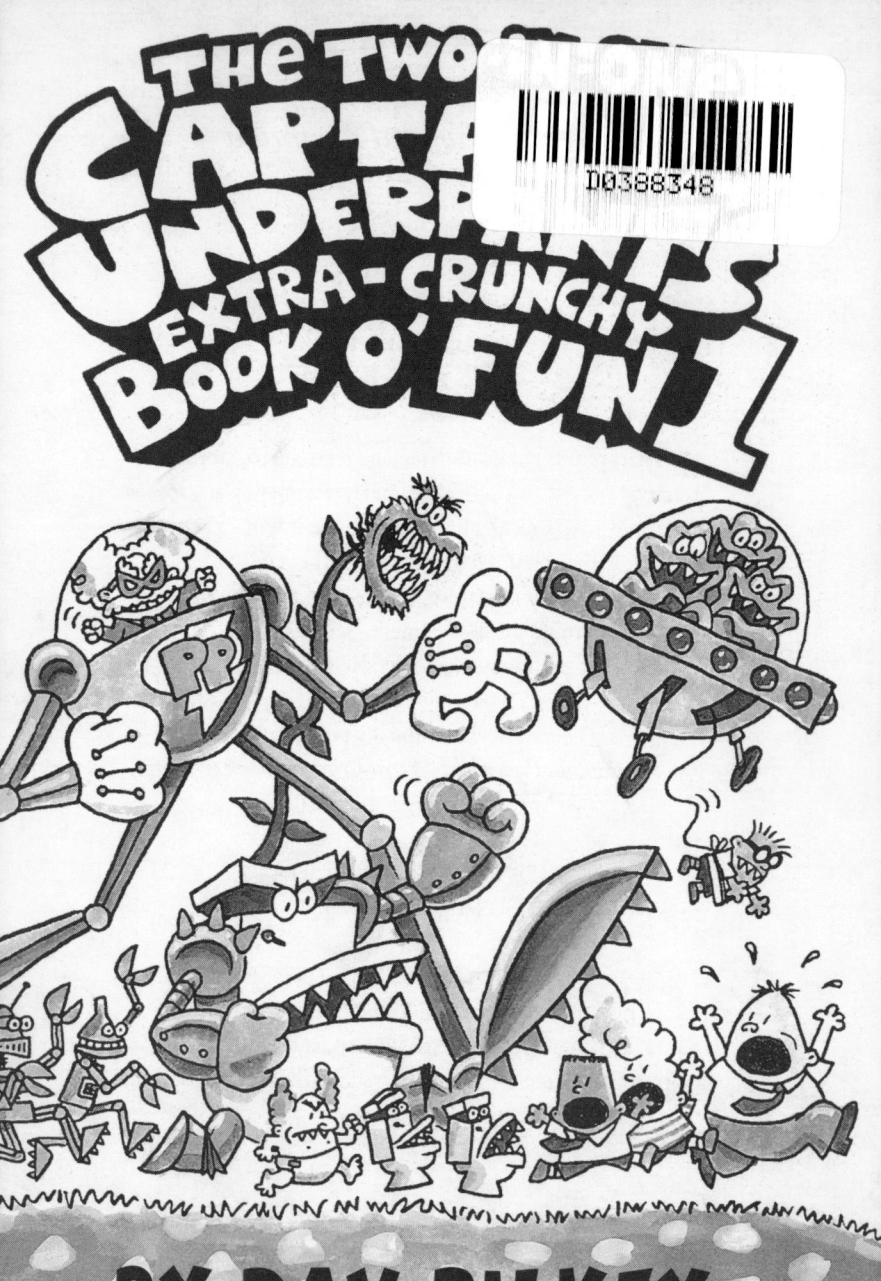

THE TWO-IN-ONE CAPTAIN UNDERPANTS EXTRA-CRUNCHY BOOK O' FUN 1

BY DAV PILKEY

The Blue Sky Press • An Imprint of Scholastic Inc. • New York

For Kathy and Anamika

THE BLUE SKY PRESS

This book was originally published as
The Captain Underpants Extra-Crunchy Book O' Fun
by the Blue Sky Press in 2001.

ISBN-13: 978-0-439-89209-4
ISBN-10: 0-439-89209-0

12 11 10 9 8 7 6 5 4 3 2 1   7 8 9 10 11 12/0

Printed in the United States of America   40

This edition first printing, October 2007

Hi everybody! After a hard day of fighting crime, I like to curl up with a really cheesy activity book like this one! In it you'll find puzzles, jokes, and lots of cool artsy-fartsy stuff. I hope you enjoy it—and remember: Never underestimate the power of underwear!

5

6

When you've figured out your story, you can start drawing your comic. This is where TEAMWORK comes in handy. I do ALL the writing 'cause I'm a good speller...

...And I do ALL the drawing because I'm a good ARTIST!

Don't worry if you make mistakes --- it happens to the best of us.

That's why they invented ERASERS.

RUB RUB RUB

Now just keep WRITING and dRAWING until you've finished telling your story.

```
L  U  M  P  Y  U  M  T  E  Y
L  O  O  P  Y  S  I  C  I  K
A  S  Z  A  S  Z  H  R  S  N
B  U  T  T  E  R  C  U  P  I
E  H  S  L  R  J  M  S  O  D
S  Q  U  E  E  Z  I  T  O  G
E  Y  F  F  P  I  H  Y  P  R
E  F  O  A  P  P  C  F  R  E
H  F  O  L  I  P  L  L  A  A
C  U  D  A  K  Y  G  U  H  S
I  L  G  F  S  T  I  N  K  Y
F  F  Y  K  R  O  D  K  V  M
S  N  P  B  L  M  G  Y  D  I
R  E  B  O  O  G  E  R  L  L
P  I  N  K  Y  T  T  O  N  S
```

(Answer on page 93)

HOW TO DRAW
CAPTAIN UNDERPANTS

7.

8.

5.

6.

3.

4.

1.

2.

16.

15.

14.
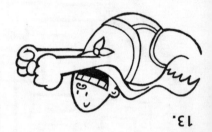

13.
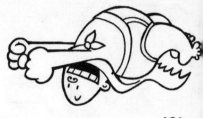

12.
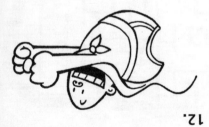

11.
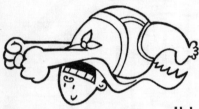

10.
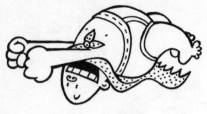

9.

15

When your victim leans back to put the penny on his chin...

...pour your water into the funnel.

...Now RUN!

-HA-HA-HA A-HA-HA-HA!

THE PERILOUS PUZZLE OF PROFESSOR POOPYPANTS

ACROSS

2. The alien spacemen were named Zorx, Klax, and _____.
4. Harold's best friend is _____.
5. "George is the kid on the left with the _____ and the flat-top."
7. George's best friend is _____.
8. Don't get "weeded out" by the Deliriously Dangerous Death-Defying _____ of Doom.
10. Dr. Diaper wanted to blow up the _____.
12. Captain Underpants is also known as a principal named Mr. _____.
14. Don't get flushed by the Turbo _____ 2000!
15. "Yum, _____, eat 'em up!"

DOWN

1. "Never underestimate the power of _____."
3. _____ Horwitz Elementary School
4. Don't get blown up by the Goosy-_____ 4000.
6. Ms. Ribble is George and Harold's _____.

7. "Harold is the one on the right with the T-shirt and the bad _____."

9. Captain Underpants fights crime with Wedgie _____.

11. Professor Poopypants's first name.

13. Don't get shrunk by the Shrinky-_____ 2000.

(Answer on page 94)

19

HOW TO DRAW
THE TURBO TOILET 2000

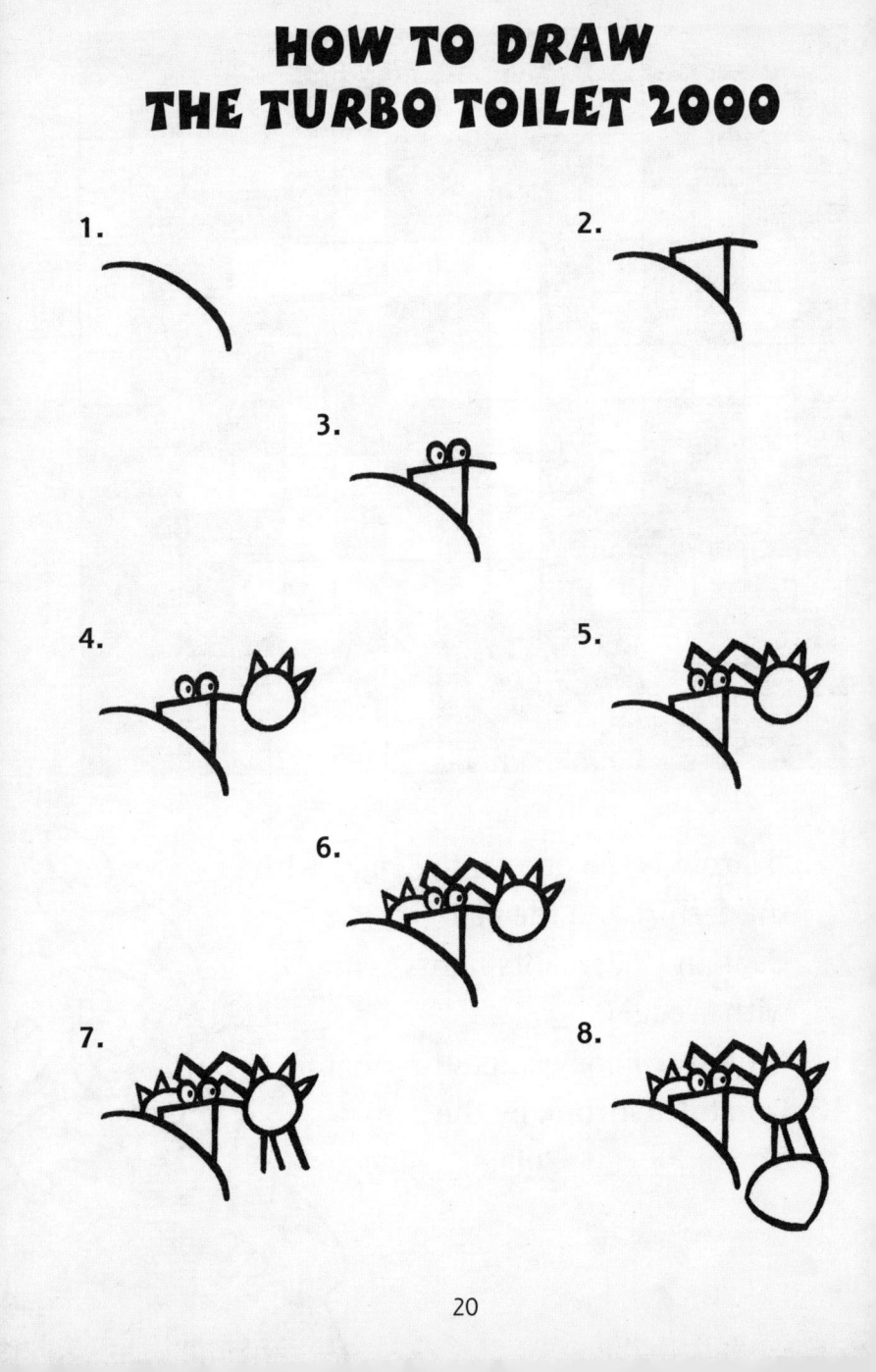

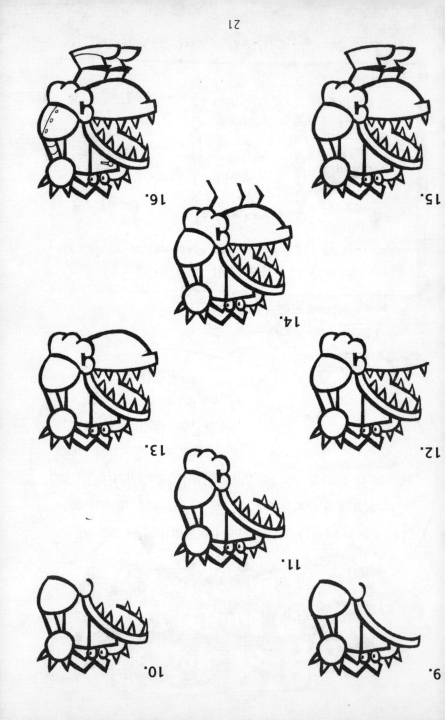

C	H	I	C	K	E	N	O	D	I	C	D
B	J	B	U	B	B	L	E	T	O	F	U
D	R	A	Z	Z	I	G	K	O	N	D	Q
L	G	E	X	N	O	I	T	C	C	R	B
A	I	D	T	R	M	I	O	I	U	R	I
N	G	Z	I	S	E	A	V	P	D	H	E
A	G	L	A	A	M	K	P	T	A	I	C
N	L	G	G	R	P	A	N	O	O	N	T
A	E	I	I	E	D	E	H	I	T	O	L
B	U	R	G	E	R	D	R	L	T	T	O
K	J	D	F	R	A	B	O	E	V	S	Y
G	E	L	K	C	I	P	I	T	V	V	R
G	Y	E	K	N	O	M	R	L	U	I	X
W	A	F	F	L	E	P	I	Z	Z	A	L

(Answer on page 94)

And since he's dribbling the ball on the floor, I'll re-draw the ball down on the floor.

HAROLD has just shown the **2ND** rule of FLIP-O-RAMA: If you want something to move, you must **RE-DRAW** it in a <u>new</u> position.

Look at HAROLD'S two drawings below... Notice the differences.

FIRST DRAWING (BOTTOM PAGE)

SECOND DRAWING (TOP PAGE)

Now flip the top page up and down to try it out.

Hey! It WORKS!!!

FLiP FLiP FLiP

NOTE: When flipping your home-made FLip-O-RamaS, ONLY FLiP The Top Page. ALso, MAKE SURE That you cAN see both pictures AS you FLip.

Top pAGe Flips up and down.

BOTTOM PAGE STAYS FLAT.

Hold here.

You might need some Adjustments To make it work better.
I'm going to draw Action Lines on The Top page.
Like any great ART, Flip-O-Rama takes Lots of Practice.
But The more You Practice, the better you'll get!
RuB RuB RuB RuB

32

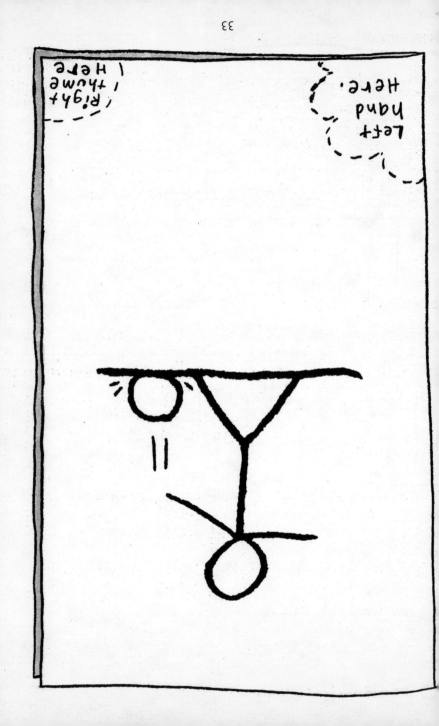

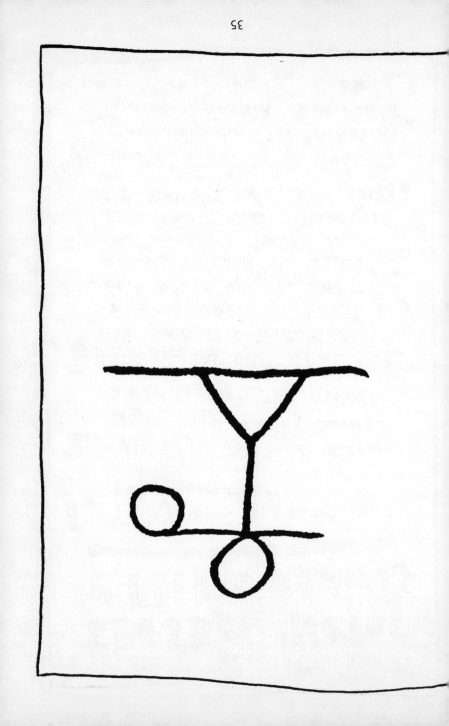

☆ ☆ SPESHEL NOTES
FOR FLIP-O-RAMISTS

1. Typing paper and notebook paper work best.

2. Although you need to trace, don't use tracing paper. It will ruin the affect.

3. Grown-ups will spaz out if your flip-o-ramas feacher "people" beating each other up. To get around this, draw <u>robots</u> and <u>monsters</u> instead. (for some reasen, Grown-ups think thats o.k. ...Go figure!)

4. You can get good ideas by studying the FLIP-O-RamAS in The "CAPtain UNDerpants" and "Ricky Ricotta" Books.

LAFFS

"Knock knock?"
"Who's there?"
"I'm a pile-up."
"I'm a pile-up who?"
"No, you're not! Don't be so hard on yourself, buddy!"

Q) What did the momma buffalo say to the baby buffalo when he went off to college?
A) Bison.

Q) What does lightning wear beneath its clothes?
A) Thunderwear.

Q) What should you do if you get swallowed by an elephant?
A) Jump up and down 'til you're all pooped out.

Q) Why did Batman cross his legs?
A) He had to go to the batroom.

Q) If you had fifty bananas in one hand, and twenty-five gallons of ice cream in the other, what would you have?
A) Really big hands.

HOW TO DRAW
PROFESSOR POOPYPANTS

1.

2.

3.

4.

5.

6.

7.

8.

9.

10.

11.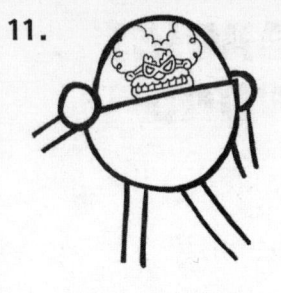

12.

13.

14.

15.

16.

THE CAFETERIA LADIES' CRAZY CROSSWORD

ACROSS

1. *The Adventures of* _____ *Underpants.*
5. Mr. Krupp was transformed into a superhero by the 3-D Hypno-_____.
6. Watch out for the Equally Evil Lunchroom _____ Nerds.
8. Pippy P. Poopypants invented the _____ Jogger 2000.
10. "Hooray for Captain _____!"
11. Don't drink the Evil Zombie Nerd _____!
13. Captain Underpants often shouts "_____-La-Laaaaa!"
14. *Cheesy Animation Technology* is more commonly known as _____-O-Rama.

DOWN

2. *The Perilous Plot of _____ Poopypants.*

3. *The Attack of the _____ Toilets.*

4. Dr. _____ was defeated soon after George shot fake doggy doo-doo at him.

7. Zorx, Klax, and Jennifer were evil guys from outer _____.

9. A popular way to misspell the word "laughs."

12. Captain Underpants wears a red _____.

(Answer on page 94)

(Answer on page 95)

43

WELCOME TO A BRAND-NEW CAPTAIN UNDERPANTS STORY . . . AND YOU'RE THE STAR!

Before you read the story on the following pages, go through and find all the blanks. Below each blank is a small description of what you need to write in the blank. Just fill in the blank with an appropriate word.

For example, if the blank looks like this:

_____ , you would think up an adjective
  (an adjective)

and put it in the blank like this: _____**stinky**_____ .
                                              (an adjective)

Remember, don't read the story first. It's more fun if you go through and fill in the blanks first, THEN read the story.

When you're done, follow the instructions at the bottom of each page to complete the illustrations. Cool, huh?

JUST FOR REMINDERS:
a **Verb** is an <u>action</u> word (like jump, swim, kick, squish, run, etc.)
an **Adjective** is a word that <u>describes</u> a person, place, or thing (lumpy, dumb, purple, hairy, etc.)

CAPTAIN UNDERPANTS VS. THE EVIL MONSTER
(STARRING GEORGE, HAROLD, AND YOU!)

Once upon a time, George, Harold, and their

friend, _____ , were busy studying
(your name)

about the wonders of_____
(an adjective)

_____ , when their new science
(disgusting things)

teacher, Mr. _____ , accidentally
(a funny name)

spilled some _____ _____
(a gross adjective)   (a liquid)

on a pile of toxic _____ .
(silly things)

(Draw yourself
sitting here)

(Draw the teacher spilling
liquid onto some toxic stuff)

Suddenly, the pile began to morph into

a giant, evil _____ .
(a silly thing)

   "Help," cried _____, "a
(somebody in your class)

giant, evil _____
(the silly thing you just used above)

just stepped on my lunchbox and ate up

_____!"
(your gym teacher's name)

   "Oh NO!" cried Mr. Krupp. "The poor

lunchbox!"

↑
(Draw the giant,
evil monster)

↖
(Draw the kid
in your class)

George, Harold, and _____
(your name)

tried to escape by hiding behind a

_____. Then _____
(a very small thing)   (your name)

snapped _____ fingers.
(either "his" or "her")

Soon, a _____ grin came
(an adjective)

across Mr. Krupp's face as he dropped

his _____ _____
(an adjective)   (an article of clothing)

and ran to his office.

↑   ↑   ↖

(Draw   (Draw the thing you're   (Draw the giant,
yourself)   all hiding behind)   evil monster)

Soon, Captain Underpants

_____ through the
(an action verb ending in "ed")

wall. He grabbed a _____
(an adjective)

_____ and hit the monster
(a thing)

on its _____ .
(a body part)

"Ouchies!" screamed the monster. It

turned and _____
(a fight move ending in "ed")

Captain Underpants on his

_____ .
(a body part)

(Draw
yourself)

(Draw the monster fighting
Captain Underpants)

48

_____ quickly mixed up a bottle
(your name)

of _____ with a jar of toxic,
(something a kid would drink)

_____ _____.
(an adjective)   (disgustings things)

"Hey, _____ ," said George,
(your name)

"where'd you find that jar of crazy stuff?!!?"

"It was right here next to this barrel of

toxic _____ _____ ,"
(an adjective)   (different disgusting things)

said _____ .
(your name)

"Oh," said Harold. "That makes sense."

↑
(Draw yourself creating
a strange mixture)

↑
(Draw the contents of the barrel
coming out the top)

49

_____ shook up the strange

mixture and threw it at the monster.

"_____!" screamed

the monster as it fell over and died of a

massive _____ attack.

"That makes sense, too," said George.

Unfortunately, some of the mixture

splashed on Captain Underpants's head,

and he turned back into Mr. Krupp.

(Draw yourself throwing the strange
concoction onto the monster)

(Draw the monster
getting splashed)

"HOLY_____ _____!"
(an adjective)   (silly animals)

shouted Mr. Krupp. "I'll bet that George,

Harold, and _____ are responsible
(your name)

for this mess!" So he punished the three kids

by making them _____ in the
(an action verb)

_____ for _____ hours.
(a room in the school)   (a number)

"This has got to be the dumbest story

we've ever been in," said George.

"Don't blame me," said Harold. "_____
(your name)

wrote it!"

↑
(Draw yourself
looking guilty)

51

ZORX, KLAX AND Jennifer's Big, BAD BATCH of Zombie Nerd Juice

OPEN

Lunar Farms ☆ ZOMBIE NERD ☆ JUICE

ULTRA-PASTEURIZED

(Answer on page 95)

52

FINAL EXAM

Hi everybody!
One thing I know for sure is that
kids LOVE to study and take tests!
That's why we've included this incredibly
difficult FINAL EXAM! Make sure you've studied
BOTH of George and Harold's College o' Art
comics. When you think you're ready, take
out a pencil, turn the page, and begin.
Good luck!

1. What's the BEST way to think up a story?

a) Create characters.

b) Put a grilled cheese sandwich on your head.

c) Roll around in steak sauce, then bark like a dog.

2. What is often to blame for creating monsters?

a) society

b) pep rallies

c) nuclear waste

3. What two things also help you think up stories?

a) brainstorming and daydreaming

b) braindreaming and daystorming

c) daybraining and dreamstorming

4. Don't worry about making mistakes. That's why they invented ____.

a) lawyers

b) erasers

c) soap-on-a-rope

5. If you have trouble writing action scenes, you can always use ____.

a) a ghost writer

b) Flip-O-Rama

c) egg salad

6. When making comics, be prepared to:

a) win friends and influence people

b) smell like Cheez Whiz™

c) suffer for your art

7. What's the world's EASIEST Flip-O-Rama?

a) a guy with a chicken up his nose

b) a guy with a basketball

c) a guy with a basketball up his nose

8. The FIRST rule of Flip-O-Rama is: If you don't want something to move, _____.

a) trace it

b) put it in a "time-out"

c) threaten to stop the car

9. The SECOND rule of Flip-O-Rama is: If you want something to move, you must _____.

a) make rude noises with your armpits

b) drink lots of prune juice

c) re-draw it in a new position

10. The more you practice, _____.

a) the better you get

b) the dumber you get

c) the stinkier you get

Now put your pencil down, and let's see how you did.

If you got at least 6 right, CONGRATULATIONS! You've just graduated from George and Harold's College o' Art.

Write to us now, and we'll send you your "P.H.D." (Pilkey Honorary Diploma), a make-it-yourself graduation cap with real artificial tassels, and a membership card. Plus, you'll have the honor of being able to write "P.H.D." after your name from now on. Lots of people have to go to real colleges, study for years, and pay thousands of dollars for that honor. But if you act now, it can all be yours absolutely FREE!

Just send a self-addressed, stamped, business-sized envelope to:

Q) Why do sharks live in saltwater?
A) Because pepper water makes them sneeze.

Q) How do you make a tissue dance?
A) Put a little boogie into it.

Q) Why did Tigger stick his head in the toilet?
A) He was looking for "Pooh."

Q) Who is Peter Pan's worst-smelling friend?
A) Stinkerbell.

Q) What nationality are you when you go to the bathroom?
A) European.

A woman walks into a pet store and says, "Can I get a puppy for my daughter?"

"Sorry, lady," says the pet store owner. "We don't do trades."

Help! Hairy Potty Just Broke Threw A window And zapped The gym Teacher.
OH, NO!!!!!! Windows ARE VALYOUBLE!
This Looks Like A JoB For...
CAPTAIN UNDERPANTS
CRASH
what Seems to Be the ProBlem, Bub?
HAiry Potty!
UH OH
THUMP
THUMP
THUMP

Finally, CAPTAin UNderpants And Hairy Potty got into A Big, terible Fight.
ROAR
TRA-LA-LAAAAA!
WARNinG
The Following Fight contains very Graphic violins.
Please cover your eyes when you turn the pages or you might get emoshinally Disterbed.
—Thank You

FLIP-O-RAMA # 1

(pages 71 And 73)

Remember, flip only page 71 While you are fliping, be sure You can See the pitcher on page 71 And the one on Page 73.

If you flip Quickly, the two pitchers will Start to look like One Animated pitcher.

Left Hand Here

The EyeBall Basher

RIGht
THUme
HERE

The Eyeball Basher

FLIP-O-RAMA #2

(pages 75 And 77)

Remember, flip _only_ page 75 while you are fliping, be sure you can see the pitcher on page 75 _And_ the one on page 77.

If you flip Quickly, the two pitchers will start to look like _One_ Animated pitcher.

Left Hand Here

THE KOO-KOO CLAP

(Right thumb here)

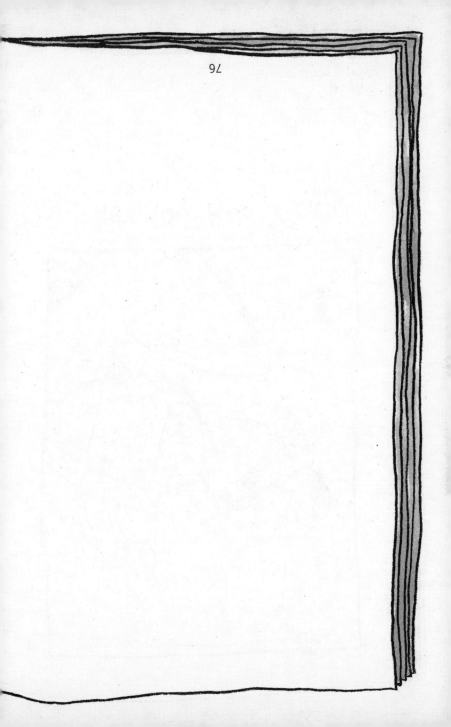

THE KOO-KOO CLAP

FLIP-O-RAMA #3

(pages 79 and 81)

Remember, flip only page 79
while you are fliping, be sure
you can see the pitcher on
page 79 And the one on
page 81.

If you flip quickly,
the two pitchers will
start to look like
one animated pitcher.

Left Hand
Here

The Potty Pounder

("Right Thumb Here")

The Potty Pounder

FLIP-O-RAMA # 4

(pages 83 and 85)

Remember, flip _only_ page 83
while you are fliping, be sure
you can see the pitcher on
page 83 _And_ the one on
page 85.

If you flip Quickly,
the two pitchers will
Start to look like
One Animated pitcher.

Left Hand
Here

The Psycko Stomp

The Psycko Stomp

HAiRy Potty ReAched down and peeled Captain UNderpants OFF OF his Foot.
YOU ARE De-Feeted!
HAW HAW HAW
NOW I AM FREE TO take OVER The world and STUFF.
So HAiRy Potty cLimbed up the taLLest BiLding he couLd Find.
SOON ever-ybody WiLL Bow down to ME!

I'M THE KING OF THE WORLD!!!
Suddenly, captain Underpants came To.
Huh?
He couldent reach his UTILITY waistband, so he had To Resort To A Sneaky Trick.
CHOMP
OWIE OWIE OUCHIES

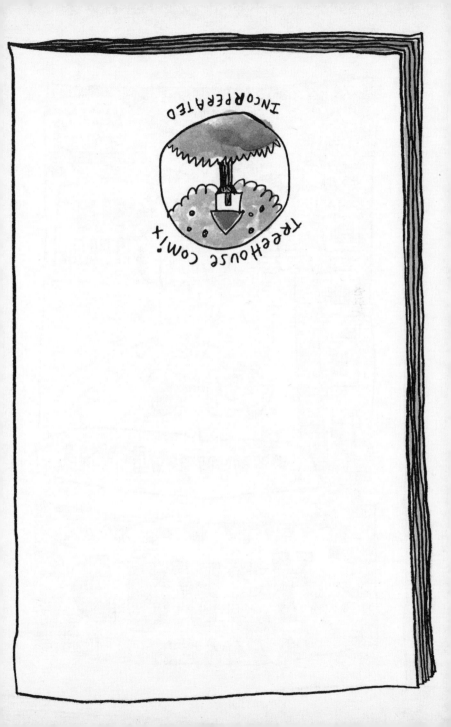

ANSWERS

**Word Find
p. 11**

```
L U M P Y U M   T E   Y
L O O P Y S I C   I S   K
A S Z A S Z H R   S   N
B U T T E R C U P   I
E H S L R J M S O   D
S Q U E E Z I T O   G
E Y F F P I H Y P   R
E F O A P P C F R   E
H F O L A P P L L A   A
C U D A K Y G L U H   S
I L G F S T I N K Y
F F Y K R O D K V M
S N P B L M G Y D I
R E B O O G E R L L
P I N K Y T T O N S
```

**Maze
p. 14**

93

**Crossword
p. 19**

**Word Find
p. 23**

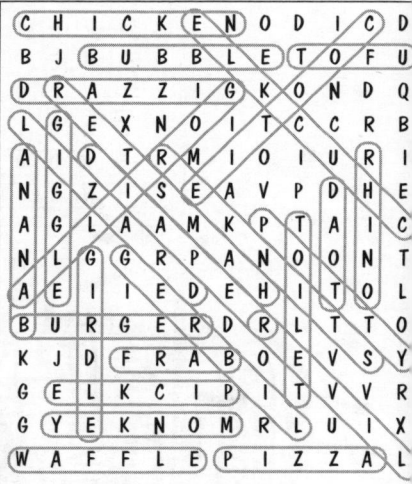

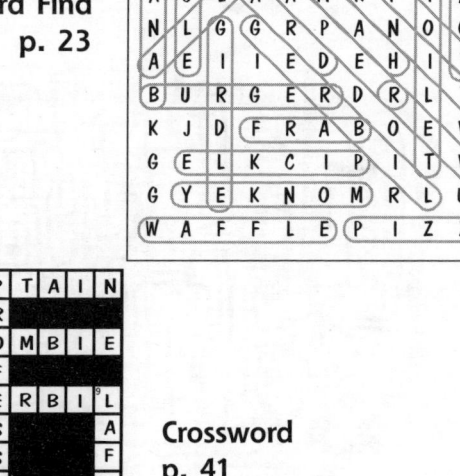

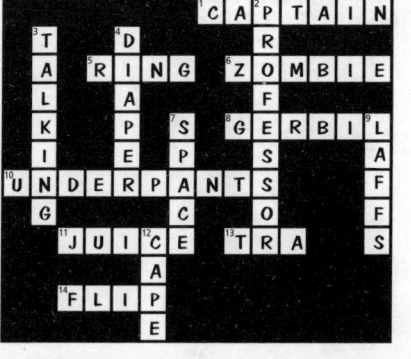

**Crossword
p. 41**

Maze p. 52

ULTRA-PASTEURIZED
ZOMBIE
NERD
JUICE
Quinoa
Jarma
OPEN

Word Find p. 43

Well, that's the end of our book. We hope you
had as much fun reading it as we had making it.
Keep writing, drawing, and flipping—and
don't forget to send away for your
free P.H.D.!